THE LUNCH CLUB

DOM PELLETIER

IT CAME FROM THE BASEMENT

FOR THE ÉDITIONS SCHOLASTIC TEAM

Scholastic Canada Ltd.
604 King Street West, Toronto, Ontario M5V 1E1, Canada

Scholastic Inc.
557 Broadway, New York, NY 10012, USA

Scholastic Australia Pty Limited
PO Box 579, Gosford, NSW 2250, Australia

Scholastic New Zealand Limited
Private Bag 94407, Botany, Manukau 2163, New Zealand

Scholastic Children's Books
Euston House, 24 Eversholt Street, London NW1 1DB, UK

www.scholastic.ca

Library and Archives Canada Cataloguing in Publication
Title: It came from the basement / Dom Pelletier.
Other titles: Navet spatial. English
Names: Pelletier, Dominique, author, artist. | Ginzburg, Dina, translator.
Description: Series statement: The lunch club ; 1 | Translation of: Le navet
spatial. Translation by Dina Ginzburg.
Identifiers: Canadiana 20200202790 | ISBN 9781443182713 (softcover)
Subjects: LCGFT: Graphic novels.
Classification: LCC PN6733.P45 N3813 2020 | DDC j741.5/971—dc23

5 4 3 2 1   Printed in Malaysia   108   20 21 22 23 24

THE LUNCH CLUB

DOM PELLETIER

IT CAME FROM THE BASEMENT

ENGLISH TEXT BY DINA GINZBURG

Scholastic Canada Ltd.

Toronto New York London Auckland Sydney
Mexico City New Delhi Hong Kong Buenos Aires

PLEASANT VALLEY
ELEMENTARY
11:59 P.M.

BRROOM!

4

I SHOULD PROBABLY AT LEAST TRY TO TALK TO SOMEONE.

HEY!

HEY, NEW KID!

HA! HA! **HA!**

HA!

HA!

HA!

WHAT'S WITH THE MUTANT PONY SHIRT?

HA! HO!

BAH-HA-HA!

HA!

SLURP

PRINCIPAL

BAM!

SO MUCH FOR PEACE AND QUIET.

THIS IS THE ONLY ROOM WITH SUPERVISION RIGHT NOW.

SO, "MR. COMEDY," YOU CAN SPEND LUNCH HERE, WRITING OUT "EATING GLUE STICKS TO MAKE MY FRIENDS LAUGH IS NOT FUNNY." ONE HUNDRED TIMES.

BUT IT WASN'T ME!

I ONLY WANT TO HEAR THE SOUND OF YOUR PENCIL, "MR. I STILL HAVE GLUE IN MY BRACES."

SLAM!

HEY, "MR. GUMMY GUMS!"

HAHA!

13

14

OK, IT'S LINE TIME! LOTS AND LOTS OF LINES...

YOU REALLY ATE A GLUE STICK?

JUST A SMALL ONE.

IT WAS HILARIOUS! TOTALLY WORTH IT!

EVERYONE LOVES A COMEDIAN.

HEY, WHO'S THAT GUY?

THE CLUB SUPERVISOR, MAYBE? I REALLY DON'T KNOW.

Z Z Z Z

SNORE

Z Z Z

HE'S BEEN ASLEEP FOR ALMOST THE ENTIRE TIME I'VE BEEN HERE.

REALLY? THAT GIVES ME AN IDEA...

Z

REAL MATURE, LEO.

SNORE...

Z Z Z

SNIFF

LUNCH

HEY! IT'S "MR. DANGER."

HA HA! WELL, PHILATELY *IS* AN EXTREME SPORT!

Philately Club

WE SHOULD CHECK OUT WHAT MR. BOB IS DOING IN THE BASEMENT.

UHHH...I UM...CAN'T. I HAVE TO AH... FINISH MY LINES.

SOMEHOW I THOUGHT YOU'D SAY THAT, SO I MADE YOU A LITTLE INVENTION.

NOW YOU HAVE NO EXCUSE. YOU'RE WELCOME!

WHAT'S IN THERE?

CRUNCH!

Philately
Club

CLANG!

HOW CAN YOU BE SMILING? WHAT HAPPENED TO "MR. VERY VERY CAUTIOUS"?

THAT WAS SO COOL! IT WAS LIKE WE WERE IN THE BEST MOVIE OF ALL TIME: *REVENGE OF THE RETURN OF THE MUTANTS FROM OUTER SPACE 3.*

THAT'S OBVIOUS.

YOU ARE GOING TO SAVE THE WORLD!

LIKE, WITH STAMPS?

DO WE MAIL IT BACK TO WHEREVER IT CAME FROM?

WHAT DO YOU PEOPLE THINK I DO HERE ALL DAY?

UM... SLEEP?

NO, "MR. 80s HAIRCUT FUNNYMAN."

I HAVE SPENT MY TIME HERE...

OVER THE YEARS, WE HAVE HAD SOME ACTUAL MEMBERS!

AND WE'VE SAVED THE WORLD AT LEAST SEVEN AND A HALF TIMES.

SAVING THE WORLD TROPHIES

*FOR THE HALF, SEE HIPPIE INVASION OF 1967

AS GUARDIAN, IT IS MY SACRED DUTY TO ADVISE CLUB MEMBERS. AND MAYBE FIND SOME.

TODAY YOU HAVE THE CHANCE TO JOIN THE COOLEST CLUB IN THE UNIVERSE! MEMBERSHIP IS FREE... AND YOU GET THIS! IT'S EVERYTHING YOU EVER WANTED TO KNOW ABOUT PHILATELY!

THE JOY OF STAMPS

LIKE HOW TO PRONOUNCE IT. IT RHYMES WITH WILL-CAT-AH-PEE. HEE HEE!

IT'S TRUE THAT WE HAVEN'T HAD A NEW MEMBER FOR A DECADE. HMM. MAYBE TWO?

BUT IT'S BEEN PRETTY QUIET ON THE WHOLE "WORLD IS SERIOUSLY AND TOTALLY DOOMED" FRONT--UNTIL NOW!

...WHERE COINCIDENTALLY, YOU TWO SHOW UP--ON THE VERY SAME DAY AS A DIRE THREAT TO ALL HUMANKIND!

IT'S NOT EVERY DAY YOU DISCOVER AN EVIL ALIEN IN THE SCHOOL BASEMENT, AMIRITE?

SO...YOU CAN HELP US? PLEASE?

53

...IN ENGLISH CLASS...

HAS ANYONE SEEN TIA AND LEO?

?

...AND IN THE BASEMENT...

DICTIONARY

ENGLISH

ENGLISH

technocrats
TECHNOLOGY n. The study and application of practical scientific knowledge, concepts, and techniques, often in relation to the field of applied sciences and engineering

...AND FIVE MINUTES LATER...

ENGLISH

ENGLISH

GAH! HOW DOES THIS THING WORK AGAIN?

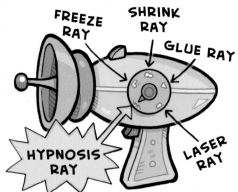

FREEZE RAY

SHRINK RAY

GLUE RAY

HYPNOSIS RAY

LASER RAY

ZAP

ARGH! ARGH! THAT'S BETTER, ISN'T IT?

MERP

FETCH ME SOMETHING TO EAT, HUMAN.

RIGHT NOW! AND DON'T YOU DARE FORGET THE MOST IMPORTANT THING!

BASEMENT

THE ALIEN!

OH YEAH, HIM...

WE'LL SPY ON HIM!

LIKE 007!

AND HOW ARE WE SUPPOSED TO DO THAT, "MR. INTERNATIONAL MAN OF MYSTERY"?

ENLIGHTEN ME WITH YOUR GENIUS...

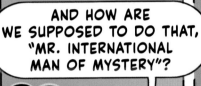

JUST LIKE THEY DO IN ALL THE BEST SPY MOVIES!

WE'LL USE THE VENTILATION DUCTS!

HELP! I'M STUCK!

ARGH!
ARGH!
ARGH!

MY PLAN IS GOING SWIMMINGLY!

FIRST I CONQUER THE SCHOOL AND THEN I TAKE OVER THE WORLD!

AND I SHALL BE CROWNED EMPEROR ZARALGAX THE FIRST!

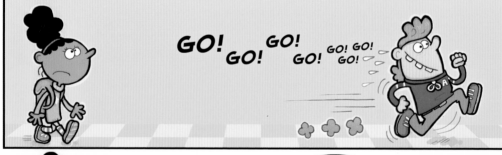

MORE BOLOGNA? *NOOOOO!*

UNACCEPTABLE! WHY SHOULD I HAVE TO SUFFER JUST BECAUSE I'M HORRIBLY ALLERGIC TO PEANUTS?

WAIT--I KNOW WHAT WILL HELP. HUMAN! FETCH ME THE SPACE KETCHUP FROM MY SPACESHIP!

IT'S PARKED IN THE WOODS BEHIND THE SCHOOL!

EVEN **YOU** CAN'T MISS IT. IT'S A SPACE TURNIP!

WHAT DO YOU MEAN, "WHY A TURNIP?"

BECAUSE IT'S THE MOST **TERRIFYING** OF ALL THE VEGETABLES!

AND BECAUSE IT WAS THE ONLY ONE ON SALE AT THE DEALERSHIP.

WHY AM I EVEN TELLING YOU ALL THIS?

GO GET ME MORE FOOD AND, ABOVE ALL, MY **KETCHUP!**

83

85

NO NEED TO FOLLOW HIM INTO THE CREEPY BASEMENT...

I'LL SPY ON HIM THROUGH THE AIR VENT!

IT'S A CLASSIC!

TONIGHT, I MAKE ONE HUNDRED PEANUT BUTTER SANDWICHES.

PHASE 3

TOMORROW, WE BRING THE SANDWICHES TO SCHOOL.

WE DISCREETLY PLACE THE "TOXIC" SANDWICHES IN MR. BOB'S CART.

GOOD PLAN!

- MR. P

I WISH I BROUGHT POPCORN!

MY PLAN IS COMING TOGETHER.

FINALLY!

NOT A MOMENT TOO SOON!

YOU ARE A VALUABLE SERVANT! I SHALL EAT YOU LAST!

POOT!

MMM... EVERYTHING IS BETTER WITH KETCHUP!

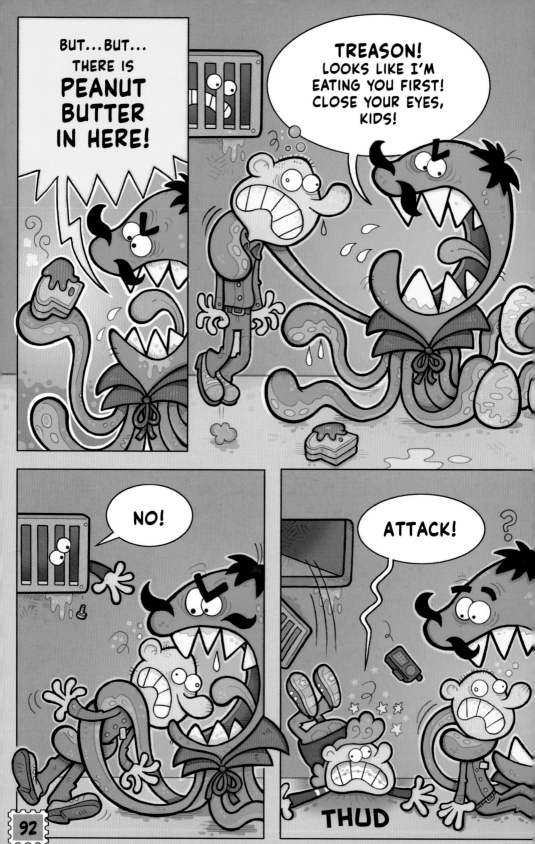

97

BRROOM!

BRRR!

BRRRR!

BRRRR!

EXPRESS DELIVERY!

NO EXTRA POSTAGE REQUIRED!

MR. PEABODY, WHAT DO WE DO WHEN WE GET THERE?

LIKE, WHAT'S THE PLAN?

BRRR!

WE IMPROVISE!

...

CRACK!

BRROOM!

I TAKE IT BACK! I LOVE TURNIPS!

LAST STOP. EVERYBODY OFF!

LET'S GO, MR. PEABODY. TIME TO...

YOU HANDLE THIS, HUMAN.

TRY THE FLASHLIGHT!

HEH HEH HEH

CLICK!

IT'S NOT WORKING! IT'S JUST MAKING HIM SCARIER!

THROW YOUR SHOE! ANYTHING! JUST SAVE YOURSELF!

OOPS!

AHHHHHHH!

PUT 'EM UP!

TIA? TIA, PLEASE SAY SOMETHING!

PULL IT TOGETHER, LEO. YOU CAN'T CRY THINGS BETTER!

ARGH!

ARGH!

ARGH!

ARGH!

I WILL BITE YOU! AND WITH MY BRACES, IT'S TOTALLY GOING TO HURT!

A PEANUT BUTTER KISS!

I'M GOING TO DIE FROM ANAPHYLAXIS. AND DISGUST!

HA! HA!

CRACK!

BAM!

HE'S NOT DEAD, JUST UNCONSCIOUS.

HE COULD COME TO AT ANY TIME.

WHAT DO WE DO WITH HIM?

WE CAN'T WAIT FOR HIM TO WAKE UP.

WE COULD SEND HIM BACK HOME, IF ONLY WE KNEW WHERE MARTIANS CAME FROM.

ACCORDING TO THE ON-BOARD COMPUTER, HE'S FROM PLUTO!

HE'S A PLUTONIAN MARTIAN?

125

126

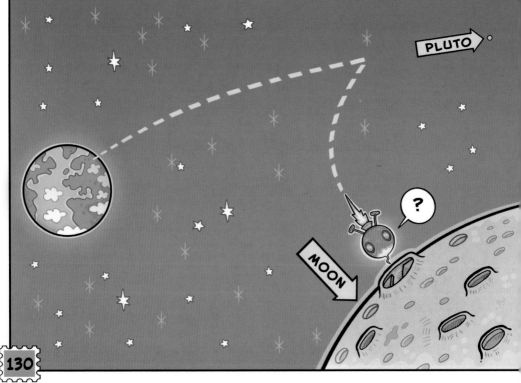